MACMILLAN
ELEMENTA

CW00339154

EDGAR ALLAN POE

Seven Stories of Mystery and Horror

Retold by Stephen Colbourn

MACMILLAN

ELEMENTARY LEVEL

Founding Editor: John Milne

The Macmillan Readers provide a choice of enjoyable reading materials for learners of English. The series is published at six levels – Starter, Beginner, Elementary, Pre-intermediate, Intermediate and Upper.

Level control

Information, structure and vocabulary are controlled to suit the students' ability at each level.

The number of words at each level:

Starter	about 300 basic words
Beginner	about 600 basic words
Elementary	about 1100 basic words
Pre-intermediate	about 1400 basic words
Intermediate	about 1600 basic words
Upper	about 2200 basic words

Vocabulary

Some difficult words and phrases in this book are important for understanding the story. Some of these words are explained in the story and some are shown in the pictures. From Pre-intermediate level upwards, words are marked with a number like this: ...³. These words are explained in the Glossary at the end of the book.

Answer keys

Answer keys for the *Points for Understanding* and the *Exercises* sections can be found at www.macmillanenglish.com

Contents

A Note About the Author

The American writer **Edgar Allan Poe** was born in Boston, in the state of Massachusetts, on January 19th 1809. He wrote poetry and stories of horror and mystery. Edgar Allan Poe had a handsome face and gray eyes. He was quiet and shy. He did not talk easily to people who he did not know.

Edgar's parents, David and Eliza, were theater actors. When Edgar was three years old, his mother died, and Edgar went to live in Richmond, Virginia. He lived with John and Frances Allan. Mr Allan was a merchant who sold tobacco. John Allan looked after Edgar, and the boy became a member of Mr Allan's family. Mr Allan was Edgar's foster-father. Later, Edgar took John Allan's last name as his own middle name.

In 1815, Edgar went with the Allans to Britain. He attended a school in London for five years. Edgar returned to America with the Allans in 1820. From 1821, he attended a school in Richmond, Virginia. He got good grades for Latin, poetry, acting and swimming.

In 1826, Edgar attended the University of Virginia. He studied languages and he was a good student. But while Edgar was at the university, he had very little money. So he gambled. He played games to win money. But he did not win enough money and soon he was in debt. Edgar owed money to many people. His foster-father would not pay Edgar's debts. Edgar and his foster-father quarreled. A year later, Edgar left the university.

Edgar joined the U.S. Army. He used the name Edgar A. Perry. In 1827, he published his first book of poetry— *Tamerlane and Other Poems*.

Edgar was in the U.S. Army for two years. First, he was

a private and later, he became a sergeant. John Allan did not want Edgar to be an ordinary soldier. He wanted Edgar to be an officer. In 1829, Mr Allan paid a sum of money to the army, and Edgar left. For a few months, Edgar went to live in Baltimore, Maryland, with his aunt, Mrs Maria Poe Clemm.

In 1830, Edgar's foster-father sent him to West Point Military Academy in Virginia. Edgar quarreled with his foster-father about this. Edgar did not want to attend West Point. He wanted to write books and poetry. But John Allan did not want Edgar to be a writer.

Edgar thought of a plan. He would not complete his duties correctly. He became a bad officer. A bad officer could not stay in the Academy. Edgar knew this. On March 6th, 1831, Edgar was dismissed from West Point.

Edgar went back to Baltimore and lived with his aunt and her daughter, Virginia Clemm. He wrote more poetry and he also started to write stories. In 1833, Edgar won fifty dollars in a writing competition. The prize was for his short story, MS *Found in a Bottle*. (MS means manuscript, a piece of writing.)

John Allan died in 1834. And the next year, Edgar became the editor of the Southern Literary Messenger in Richmond. He read articles, short stories and books. Then he wrote about them in the magazine. The following year, twenty-seven-year-old Edgar married his cousin, Virginia Clemm. She was thirteen years old.

Virginia, Edgar, and his aunt moved to New York City in January 1837. In 1838, they moved again. They went to Philadelphia in New Jersey. In that year, Edgar's novel, *The Narrative of Arthur Gordon Pym*, was published. He worked as an editor for Burton's Gentleman's Magazine and

Graham's Magazine. In 1842, Poe met the famous British author, Charles Dickens, and talked to him about his work.

In April 1844, the Poe family moved back to New York. Edgar worked for the newspaper, the *New York Evening Mirror*. The following year, Poe's most famous poem, *The Raven*, was published. After this, Poe became well known in Europe as well as America.

Some of Poe's poems are:

Al Aaraaf, Tamerlane and Minor Poems (1829)
To Helen (1831)
The Raven (1845)
The Bells (1849)

Some of Poe's stories are:

Ligeia (1838)
The Narrative of Arthur Gordon Pym (1837)
Tales of the Grotesque and Arabesque (1840)
The Murders in the Rue Morgue (1841)
The Pit and the Pendulum (1842)
The Masque of the Red Death (1842)
The Gold Bug (1843)
The Black Cat (1843)

1846 was a bad year for Poe. He stopped publishing his own magazine, the Broadway Journal, because it had not been successful. Then his wife Virginia became very ill.

On January 30th, 1847, Virginia died and Edgar started drinking too much alcohol. He became very ill. All his life, Poe had trouble with money and alcohol. When he was worried and upset, he drank alcohol. Alcohol made him very ill. He had terrible dreams.

Edgar Allan Poe was famous for his tales of detection and mystery. And there was a mystery about his own death. In the summer of 1849, Poe visited the cities of

Norfolk and Richmond. He talked about his work, and then he met some friends. He told them that he was going to marry Sarah Shelton. Edgar had known Sarah for more than twenty years.

On September 27th, Poe left Richmond and traveled to New York. Three days later, someone found Edgar lying in a street in Baltimore. He was very ill and he was wearing someone else's clothes. The clothes were too small for him and they were of poor quality. Many people believed that Poe's own clothes had been stolen.

Poe was taken to a hospital but he never got well. On the fourth night, he called out the name "Reynolds" loudly. Early in the morning of October 7th, 1849, Edgar Allan Poe said a prayer and died.

A Note About These Stories

Edgar Allan Poe was interested in fear and death. He was also interested in ghosts and strange events. His stories about the frightening and terrible things that happen to people were very popular with Europeans and Americans. Famous writers and poets such as Robert Louis Stevenson, Oscar Wilde and Charles Baudelaire thought well of his work. Many of Poe's short stories have been made into movies.

Some of Poe's tales are about characters who try to find murderers or thieves. These tales are some of the first detective stories that were written by an American. Edgar Allan Poe was also one of the first American authors who wrote a science fiction story. In the nineteenth century, there were many new ideas about science, philosophy and religion. Poe was interested in these ideas. He used them in some of his stories.

In *The Pit and the Pendulum*, Poe tells the story of a man who is questioned by members of the Inquisition. The Inquisition asked people questions about their belief in the Roman Catholic religion. From the fifteenth century to the seventeenth century, inquisitors made sure that everyone followed the laws of the Roman Catholic Church. They tried to find people who did not agree with the church. Inquisitors punished anyone who did not follow the church's laws. As the inquisitors asked their questions, they tortured the people. The inquisitors did terrible, painful things to the peoples' bodies. Many people died when they were tortured.

The Gold Bug is a detective story about a secret message and golden treasure. A pirate—a thief who sailed on the seas—has hidden gold, money and jewels. The pirate in *The Gold Bug* is named Captain William Kidd. William Kidd was born in Scotland in 1645. He died in England in 1701.

For hundreds of years, pirates attacked sailing ships that carried goods and gold. The pirates' own ships were faster and they had more powerful guns. Pirates' ships often had a black flag with a picture of a white skull and bones on it. Both men and women became pirate captains. Some of the most famous pirates were William Kidd, Anne Bonny, Blackbeard, Mary Read, Henry Morgan, and Barbarossa. Pirates fought and killed many thousands of sailors and they stole many ships. They took everything valuable from the ships. But pirates loved gold more than anything. Often they hid their gold in the ground.

In *The Facts in the Case of Mr Valdemar*, Poe writes about hypnotism. In the nineteenth century, this was a popular new way of helping sick people.

When a person is hypnotized, they are made to sleep. While the person is sleeping, a hypnotist tells the person what to do. Hypnotized people believe what a hypnotist tells them.

The Masque of the Red Death is a strange tale about a huge party—a masque. Hundreds of years ago, masques took place in castles or houses that belonged to rich and important rulers. Music was played at a masque. The guests wore brightly colored clothes and danced together. They also wore masks—coverings over their faces. When they wore masks, none of the guests knew each other.

A Map of The United States

A Picture Dictionary

skull and crossed bones

pirate

barrel

telescope

peg

lantern

treasure

tape measure

shovel

pickax

sailing ship

mast

oars

coffin   rowboat

spider's
web

mask

rat

11

scarab beetle

Rainbow

cliff ledge

creek branch

bridge

pendulum hourglass guitar goat

scythe

lamp compass

whale

12

THE PIT AND THE PENDULUM

I opened my eyes. But I could not see anything. It was dark—completely dark. There was no light at all. Everything was black. I closed my eyes and opened them again. But I could see nothing. Where was I?

I was lying on my back. I was lying on something hard and cold. I reached out my hand and felt a stone floor. The stones were cold and damp. I was lying on my back in a stone room. Was I in a tomb? Was I in a place where dead bodies were buried? I had to move. I had to find out. I turned over onto my hands and knees. Then I started to crawl forwards. In a few seconds, I found a wall. It was cold and wet. Maybe I was in a room that was under the ground.

I followed the wall, very slowly. I thought that I was moving in a circle. I was not sure. Then I had an idea. I tore a piece of cloth from my shirt and put it on the floor, near the wall. Then I walked along the wall of the room.

I counted the number of times that I moved my hands forward. Twenty…thirty…forty times. Where was the piece of cloth? Had I gone past it in the dark? Had I gone around the room twice? I counted up to one hundred before I found the piece of cloth. But I did not find a dead body in a coffin. I was not in a tomb.

Where was I? I tried to remember. I remembered that I was in Toledo, in Spain. Then I remembered a courtroom and men in red gowns. They had asked questions—more and more questions. Their voices were soft and their eyes were bright. How many hours had they questioned me? How many *days* had they questioned me? I could not remember. The questions had gone on and on. But what was my crime? What law had I broken? I did not know. I was very frightened. I thought that the questioners were going to torture me. But no one had cut me with sharp blades. No one had hit me. No one had burnt me with hot iron. Now I must be in a jail. This room was a prison cell. Maybe I would die here, without food, or water, or light.

I closed my eyes again and I must have slept.

———

When I awoke, I moved my foot and it hit something. I touched a loaf of bread and a pitcher of water. A jailer had come into my prison cell and left food and drink.

I knew that my prison cell was large. But what was in the center? For a few minutes, I sat with my back against the wall. Then I started to crawl straight ahead—across the floor of the cell. I moved very slowly. Suddenly, my hand went down and forward. I had found a hole—a pit in the floor. I could feel and smell damp air. The air was rising up from the pit. I guessed that the pit was very deep. I had almost fallen into it. My body shook with fear. My skin was covered with sweat. The drops of sweat fell from my face and down into the deep hole.

Suddenly, I heard a noise. A small door opened above my head and light shone down on me. For a few seconds, I saw my prison cell. Then the small door shut again and everything was dark and black. I was right! I was in a room with a deep pit in its center.

I understood now. My torturers had been waiting and watching. They wanted me to jump into the deep pit. They wanted me to end my life.

I slowly crawled back to the pitcher of water and the bread. My arms and legs were shaking. I was weak and tired. I took a piece of bread and started to eat. The bread tasted of salt. I quickly drank the water from the pitcher. Soon after this I felt very, very tired. I slept again.

———

When I awoke, the cell was not completely dark. I could just see its walls. The room was square. Each wall was about fifteen feet long. And the walls were not made of stone. They were made of metal. High in the center of the ceiling, there was a small door. Strange and terrible pictures were carved into the metal walls. The pictures were of evil spirits and monsters.

I was lying on my back but I could not get up. I was no longer lying on the stone floor. My body was tied to a wooden bed. A rope was tied around my chest, but I could move my arms. I reached out my hands and tried to find the pitcher of water. I was very thirsty.

There was no water, but I found a dish of meat. I put a piece of the meat into my mouth. No! I could not eat the meat! It tasted terrible. It was full of salt and strong spices. My jailers wanted me to be thirsty. This was a new torture.

I looked up at the ceiling. I could see a picture there. It was a picture of Time—an old man with a long beard. Pictures of Time always showed an old, bearded man with an hourglass in his hand. Hourglasses had two containers inside them. The containers were made of glass and they were joined in the center. One of the containers was filled with sand. When all the sand had run from one container to the other, an hour had passed.

Time also held a long, sharp scythe. Every living thing is killed by Time.

But in the picture on the ceiling, the blade of Time's scythe was not part of the painting. This blade was real, and it was sharp. It was made of metal and it hung down from the ceiling. The blade was like the pendulum of an

I could see a picture of Time.

old clock. As I watched, the pendulum started to move. It moved slowly, backward...and forward.

Suddenly I heard a noise beside me. It was the sound of many small animals running on hard ground. Then I heard high, sharp cries. Rats! There were rats here in the cell! They had climbed out of the pit!

Several large black rats ran across the floor toward my wooden bed. I moved my arms and shouted. I tried to frighten them away. The rats looked at me with their red eyes. They opened their mouths, and I saw their sharp, pointed teeth. Were the rats going to be my next torture?

I looked up at the pendulum again. It was moving more quickly now. As it moved backward and forward, it made a soft whooshing sound. WHOOSH! The pendulum swung back behind my head, and I could not see it. Then it swung forward over my feet. WHOOSH! As I watched, I saw that the pendulum was lower. Very slowly, the pendulum was getting closer to me. Now I saw the reason for the pendulum. *This* was how I was going to die! The sharp blade of the pendulum was going to kill me. But it was not going to kill me quickly. It was going to cut my body very, very slowly. The pain would be terrible. How many times was the blade going to cut my body? How long was I going to lie on the wooden bed? How many times was I going to scream, as my blood ran onto the floor?

One of the rats ran over my hand. I cried out and pulled my hand away quickly. The dish of meat was still beside me. The rats could smell the meat and they wanted it.

Suddenly I had an idea. I reached out my hand and took some of the meat from the dish. Then I rubbed the spiced meat onto the rope that was around my body. I rubbed the meat all along the rope. Then I lifted my hands above my head and lay still.

At first, the rats were frightened of me. They did not come too close. Then one of them jumped onto my chest. I did not move. I felt the rat's sharp little feet on my body. I saw its red eyes and sharp teeth. I tried not to scream.

The rat put its nose closer to the rope. It smelled the spiced meat on the rope. The rat started to bite the rope with its sharp teeth. It was eating the meat that was on the rope. Soon another rat jumped onto me. It started to eat the rope too.

More and more rats came. They ran over my face. They ran over my body. I kept my mouth and eyes closed. I tried not to shout in fear. I tried to stop my body shaking. The rats' feet and tails touched me. I felt the horrible animals on my mouth and my eyes and my nose. I heard their high, sharp cries.

The sound of the pendulum became louder. Soon, the whooshing sound of the pendulum was louder than the sound of the rats. The blade was coming closer to my body. I felt the air move as the pendulum passed over my face.

The pendulum swung very wide. I counted each time that it passed over me. Six seconds…seven seconds—then the blade swung back. Six…seven…WHOOSH! Six…seven…WHOOSH! The pendulum swung lower and lower. It was now only a few inches above me. And it was moving more slowly.

The huge blade frightened the rats and they ran away. The animals knew that they were in danger. They had eaten part of the rope, but I was not yet free. I waited for the pendulum to cut the rope completely.

Seven seconds…eight seconds. The pendulum whooshed above my body from head to foot—and then from foot to head. Seven…eight…WHOOSH! It was very close to me now. I tried to make my body lower on the

The rat started to bite the rope with its sharp teeth.

bed. Where was the blade of the pendulum going to bite me? Was it going to cut my head? Was it going to cut my chest or stomach? I screamed. The blade bit and it cut the rope! The pendulum swung toward my feet.

Suddenly I was free. I jumped from the wooden bed and lay on the floor. Sweat was pouring from my skin. I was breathing quickly. The pendulum whooshed past one more time, and then it stopped.

The small door in the ceiling was open. My torturers were watching. They had seen me escape from the blade. Suddenly, the pendulum moved up into the ceiling, and it was still.

I was not safe for long. A little later, I smelt something. It was not the smell of rats. And it was not the smell from the deep, dark pit. It was the smell of hot iron.

The metal walls of the cell were becoming hot! I moved closer to the pit. It was cooler here. This was my torturers' plan. They were heating the walls. When the cell became too hot, I must jump into the pit. The pit was cool and damp. But the cell walls were not only hot, they were also moving! The hot metal walls were moving toward me. The pictures of the evil spirits and monsters were now red. They were getting hotter. I was going to burn on the walls, or I was going to fall into the pit. I had very little time.

I stood on the edge of the pit and I closed my eyes. The walls were hot and the floor was hot. The air was hot! I felt the terrible heat on the skin of my face and hands. I was ready to fall. This was the end. I was going to die in this terrible place.

Suddenly, I heard voices. People were shouting. I heard the sounds of guns. People were fighting. Then I heard another sound. The walls were moving again.

What was happening now? I was weak and tired. My arms and legs were shaking. The walls were moving back, but it was too late. My clothes were starting to burn. I was about to fall. I was already falling...

Then someone held my arm and pulled me back. As I turned my head, I saw the person who was holding me. It was a soldier who was wearing the uniform of the French army. French soldiers had captured the city of Toledo. All the prisoners were free.

THE GOLD BUG

I first met Mr William Legrand many years ago. He lived on Sullivan's Island, near Charleston. The island is in the Atlantic Ocean, opposite the coast of South Carolina.

Sullivan's Island is small. It is three miles long and three-quarters of a mile wide. A creek—a narrow area of sea—lies between the island and the mainland. There was only one large building on Sullivan's Island—Fort Moultrie. A group of soldiers lived in this large wooden building on the western side of the island. The soldiers in Fort Moultrie guarded the coast of South Carolina from our enemies.

William Legrand had been very rich, but he lost all his money. His fine house and property in New Orleans was sold and he left the state of Louisiana. Soon after this, he moved to Sullivan's Island.

Legrand had no family. His parents were dead and he had no brothers or sisters. He was not married and he had no children. He lived with a servant named Jupiter. Legrand and Jupiter lived in a small wooden house by the edge of the sea. They caught fish and birds for food. Charleston was not far, but they did not often go there.

I lived in Charleston and sometimes I visited Legrand. I crossed the creek to the island in a small boat.

William Legrand was an interesting man who had a good education. But he was also a strange man. Legrand enjoyed living in this quiet place because he did not like meeting people. Often, he did not speak for several days. Sometimes he became excited and talked for many hours. When I visited Sullivan's Island, Legrand and I talked about many things. We talked about books that he had read. He talked about the animals, birds and insects near his home. He drew pictures of the creatures that he saw on the island.

One day in the month of October, I went to visit Legrand. But when I got to his home, no one was there. It was a cold day, so I went into Legrand's little wooden house. Then I lit a fire and waited for him.

Legrand and Jupiter returned late in the afternoon. They had been walking by the edge of the sea and they had found an unusual bug. Legrand was very excited by this insect.

"It has strange patterns on its back," he said.

"Can I see it?" I asked.

"No, I'm sorry," replied Legrand. "You can't see it tonight. I showed it to Lieutenant Gray this afternoon. He is interested in all kinds of insects. He has taken the bug to the fort. He has a book about insects. But I don't think that he will find any information about this bug in his book."

"What is unusual about the bug?" I asked.

"I'll draw a picture of it," said Legrand.

He took a pen from his pocket and looked for a piece of paper. But he could not find any pieces of paper in his desk.

"Oh, I remember," he said. He put his hand in another pocket of his coat and found a piece of paper. Then he drew a picture of the bug very carefully. The picture showed a beetle with a round body and six legs. On its back there were three strange marks.

"You draw well," I said. "That is a scarab, I'm sure. Scarabs have round bodies that are covered in hard shells. Thousands of years ago, the people of Egypt believed that scarabs had magical powers."

The picture showed a beetle. On its back there were three strange marks.

"That bug was never alive," said Jupiter suddenly. "It's made of metal—gold. I've never held such a heavy bug."

"Don't listen to Jupiter," said Legrand. "Maybe the bug is a scarab. And yes, it is a golden color. But it has these very unusual marks on its back—three black spots. There are two small spots above a larger spot. The spots are like two eyes and a mouth. It's a pattern of a skull—the head of a dead man. A picture of a skull is sometimes called a death's head. I have discovered a bug that no one has seen before!"

I took the paper and looked at the drawing. It was now late. Outside, it was almost dark. I went closer to the fire and held the paper near to the light of the flames. Now I could see the drawing more clearly.

The paper was very old and thick. It was made of an animal's skin. I saw the three spots on Legrand's drawing of the bug. It certainly had a pattern of a skull—a death's head. I also saw some writing in red ink. I had not seen the writing earlier.

"What do these strange letters mean?" I asked. I gave the paper back to Legrand.

Legrand stared at the paper for several minutes. But he did not say anything. He did not speak about the bug or the picture again. He did not speak to me at all for the rest of the evening.

I thought that he wanted to be alone. So, the next morning, I said goodbye to him and Jupiter. Then I left Sullivan's Island and returned to Charleston. I thought no more about the picture of the bug, or the red writing.

———

About a month later, Jupiter came to Charleston. This was unusual. Jupiter did not leave Sullivan's Island often, and he never came to Charleston alone. He came to see me.

"Is anything wrong?" I asked him.

"Mr Legrand is sick," said Jupiter.

"Does he have a fever?"

"No, he's sick in his mind," Jupiter replied. "He walks about the island. He takes the boat across the creek to the mainland. He won't eat and he doesn't sleep. His face is pale—like a ghost. All day and all night he writes numbers and letters in a book. He only talks about the gold bug and a death's head. The bug has made Mr Legrand mad. Mr Legrand has sent me here. He has written this note to you."

I opened the note and read these words:

Dear friend

I was not polite when you visited me. I'm sorry about that. But I must speak to you again. Please come to Sullivan's Island. I have something very important to tell you. Poor Jupiter is worried about me, but I'm not sick. Come to my home immediately and I'll tell you my news.

William Legrand

I went to Sullivan's Island with Jupiter immediately. I found Legrand sitting in his wooden house. He did not look sick. He was not lying in his bed. He was sitting at a table. He was looking at something on the table in front of him. Then he wrote in a small book.

"Are you well?" I asked.

"I'm very well," Legrand said quickly. His eyes were bright and shining. "I'm glad that you have come. Look at this."

He showed me a golden beetle that was lying on the table.

"That is the gold bug!" said Jupiter.

The golden insect was very heavy. Was it made of gold?

"I've studied the beetle," said Legrand. "But I've also studied this paper."

Legrand picked up the piece of thick, old paper that had his drawing on it.

"On the day of your visit, I found the bug when I was walking with Jupiter," said Legrand. "We were by the sea. The bug was lying on the ground. A few feet further along, there was a boat. The boat was very old and broken, and it was lying on the edge of the sea. In the bottom of the boat there was this piece of paper. I put the bug in the paper and put them both in my pocket. A few minutes later, we met the lieutenant from the fort. I gave him the bug because he wanted to study it. Then Jupiter and I went back to the house."

"When we talked about the bug, I wanted to make a drawing for you," Legrand went on. "But I had no paper. Then I remembered the paper in my pocket. I drew my picture on one side of the paper. I did not know that there were some letters in red ink on the other side of the paper. You held the paper near to the heat of the fire. This made the letters clearer. Then you gave the paper back to me. Since that evening, I've studied that writing."

"I don't understand," I said. "Please explain."

Legrand was excited. He started to speak quickly.

"I believe that the gold bug has magic powers," he said. "It's showing us the way to something very important. The gold bug, the skull pattern on its back, and the red letters on the paper. These are all clues—important pieces of information. That is what I think. The clues will show us where to find something that is very valuable. Come with me and Jupiter."

"Where are we going?" I asked. But Legrand did not

answer. Maybe Jupiter was right. Maybe Legrand *was* mad.

I followed the two men to their little rowboat that was outside the house. There were some tools in the bottom of the boat—two shovels and a pickax.

I looked at the tools. "Are we going to dig a hole in the ground?" I asked. But Legrand did not reply. He started to push the boat down into the sea.

Legrand, Jupiter and I got into the boat. Jupiter pulled on the oars and the boat started to move away from the island. Many times, Legrand looked at a compass. Sometimes he asked Jupiter to row the boat further toward the north.

When we had crossed the creek to the mainland, we pulled the boat up out of the water. Then we walked for about two hours. Again and again, Legrand looked at the compass in his hand. I did not speak and neither did Jupiter. A few times Legrand said the words, "Good! Good!"

I became tired and I wanted to return home. What was the reason for this journey? I could not guess.

As the sun was setting, we came to a tall cliff that rose up from the land. The light of the sun shone onto the side of the cliff. We could see a flat, narrow ledge on the cliff's side. The ledge was like a wide mouth in the rock.

Trees surrounded the tall cliff. One tree was very tall and very, very old.

Legrand took us toward the tall tree and stopped. He looked up at its branches.

"Can you climb that tree?" Legrand asked Jupiter.

"I can climb any tree," Jupiter answered.

"Very well, Jupiter. Take the gold bug and climb the tree," said Legrand to his servant. "Climb the tree and tell me what you can see."

Legrand gave the golden insect to Jupiter. There was a piece of string around the bug.

Jupiter started to climb the tree. I watched him as he went up and up. Soon we could not see him.

"Jupiter!" Legrand called out. "How many branches have you climbed?"

"I'm on the sixth branch," Jupiter replied.

"Climb to the seventh branch on the east side of the tree. Then look along that branch of the tree," Legrand said excitedly. "Can you see anything on the branch?"

"There's something white!" Jupiter shouted. "Oh, sir! It's a skull! A dead man's head is sitting on this branch. The skull is fixed to the branch. Someone took a dead man's head up here!"

"Good. Drop the bug into the left eye of the skull," Legrand shouted to Jupiter.

"But the bug will fall down!" Jupiter replied.

"Yes, yes!" Legrand shouted. "I want the bug to fall to the ground."

"Yes, sir," Jupiter said. "I'm dropping the bug now."

Legrand watched very carefully. The bug was heavy. I heard it fall. We both saw the gold bug shining as it lay on the ground.

"You can come down now, Jupiter," he said. "I've got the bug."

Legrand put a wooden peg in the ground where the gold insect fell.

"Now we must measure fifty feet from the tree," said Legrand.

He took a tape measure from his pocket. He put one end of the tape measure against the tree and laid it out along the ground, toward the peg. Where the tape measure measured fifty feet, Legrand stopped.

"I'm dropping the bug now."

"Dig here," he said.

Jupiter took the pickax and started to dig. He soon hit something in the ground.

"Oh, sir," he said. "More bones of a dead man."

I saw long bones and a skull. Legrand removed the bones from the hole. Then he picked up a shovel.

"Dig deeper, Jupiter," he said.

I saw the blade of a knife. Then I saw three or four old coins. They looked like pieces of gold.

The sun was very low in the sky now. It was almost dark. I lit a lantern and held it above my head. The light shone down into the deep hole.

Soon there was a sharp sound. Legrand's shovel had hit wood and metal.

"My shovel has touched something," he said. "It's a box." Then he removed more soil from the hole.

After a few minutes, I saw a wooden box with handles made of metal. It was very heavy and Legrand and Jupiter could not lift it. But Legrand pulled open the lid of the box and looked inside.

I held the lantern nearer to the box and looked closer. Inside the box there was wonderful treasure! There were gold and silver coins, and beautiful jewels! I was shocked. Legrand put his hands into the box and laughed.

"We'll take this treasure back to Sullivan's Island," he said. "We'll take as many of the coins and jewels as we can carry. Then we'll come back for more."

I forgot that I was tired. I was excited. We carried about one third of the treasure back to the rowboat. Then went back to Sullivan's Island and put the gold, silver and jewels in Legrand's house.

We made two more journeys to the mainland. Each time, we took away another third of the treasure. As we returned to Sullivan's Island for the third time, the sun was rising. By dawn, we were exhausted. But all the treasure was in Legrand's house. Then the three of us, Legrand, Jupiter and I, slept for several hours.

When we awoke, we looked at the treasure. Legrand started counting the coins and jewels.

"Legrand, how did you know about this treasure?" I asked. "And how did you know where to look for it?"

"The old paper gave me the clues," Legrand said. "And you helped me to understand the clues."

"But I did nothing," I said.

"You're wrong," said Legrand. "You held the paper close to the fire. There's secret writing on the paper. When the paper became hot, the writing became red."

Legrand took the old piece of paper from his pocket and put it on the table.

"Look," he said. And he pointed at lines of letters, numbers and marks that were written in red ink.

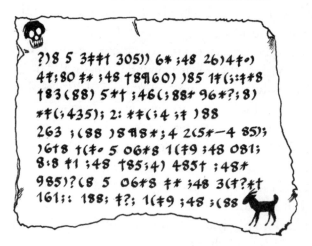

"There are also two small pictures with the message," Legrand said. "At the beginning of the message there's a picture of a skull—a death's head. Pirates used skulls—death's heads to frighten people. Pirates put black flags with pictures of white skulls and bones on their ships."

Legrand smiled. Then he went on. "At the end of the message there's a picture of a small goat. The word for a young goat is a KID. One of the most famous pirates was Captain Kidd. The drawing of the goat is a picture word for Captain Kidd's name."

"Captain William Kidd sailed along this coast in the seventeenth century," I said. "People believed that he buried some of his treasure somewhere in South Carolina. This is a message about his treasure!"

"Yes!" replied Legrand. "I believe that too. After I'd seen those pictures, I looked more closely at the message. I worked for a very long time."

"E is the most common letter in the English language," said Legrand. "E is used most frequently in the spelling of English words. The next letter that is used most frequently is A. After that, the most frequent letter is O, then I. The order of frequency is this: A O I D H N R S T U Y C F G L M W B K P Q X Z J V. The number 8 appears forty-one times in this message. I decided that the number 8 must be the letter E. After many hours, I discovered the code for these letters. This is the code."

Legrand showed me the code that he had written:

A	B	C	D	E	F	G	H	I	J	K	L
5	2	—	†	8	1	3	4	6			0

M	N	O	P	Q	R	S	T	U	V	W	X	Y	Z
9	*	‡	•		(	)	;	?	¶				:

"At last I understood the message," he said. "This is what it said."

Legrand took a paper from his desk and put it in front of me. I read these words:

USE A GOOD GLASS IN THE BISHOPS
HOTEL ON THE DEVILS SEAT FORTYONE
DEGREES AND THIRTEEN MINUTES
NORTHEAST BY NORTH TO SEE
BIG TREE SEVENTH BRANCH EAST
SIDE DROP A LINE FROM THE LEFT
EYE OF THE DEATHS HEAD THEN
MEASURE A LINE ON THE GROUND
FIFTY FEET OUT FROM THE TREE

"Where are the Bishop's Hotel and the Devil's Seat?" I asked. "I've never heard of these places."

"More than one hundred and forty years ago, a man named Bishop lived in this area," said Legrand. "Mr Bishop had a hotel—an inn—on the top of a tall cliff. People went to the inn to drink."

"On the cliff, near Bishop's inn, there was a ledge in the rock," Legrand said. "The ledge was called the Devil's Seat. Some people believed that the pirate, Captain William Kidd, visited the inn. He sat on the ledge in the rock. He watched the ships sailing along the coast."

"I read the message again," said Legrand. "I looked at the words: 'Use a good glass.' You drink from a glass. But there is another meaning. 'Glass' is an old word for a 'telescope'. Sailors used telescopes to see things that were far away."

"Did you find Bishop's Hotel and the Devil's Seat?" I asked quickly.

"Yes," Legrand replied. "I found the tall cliff and the ledge—the Devil's Seat. Bishop's inn disappeared a long time ago. I sat down on the ledge and I looked through a telescope. I looked towards the northeast. Then I saw a tall tree. There was something white on one of the branches. I became very excited. Soon after this I returned to Sullivan's Island, and I wrote you a note."

"The bodies with the treasure!" I said suddenly. "The skull and the bones in the ground! Do you think that they were the bodies of pirates?"

"Yes," Legrand said. "I think that those bodies must be two pirates from Kidd's ship. Kidd killed them when he buried his treasure near the tree. Now we must decide how to spend his money! We are all rich!"

THE FACTS IN THE CASE OF MR VALDEMAR

I am a scientist and I am a hypnotist. I am interested in hypnotism. Hypnotism helps sick people as they sleep. That is what I believe. Some patients have an illness in their bodies. Some patients are sick in their minds. When a patient is hypnotized they can help themselves.

As the patient sleeps, he or she listens to the words of the hypnotist. The patients' own thoughts can help their minds and bodies to get well.

This is the way that I make my patients sleep. First, I move my hands in front of the patient's face. Then I speak slowly and clearly. My voice is deep and soft.

"Your eyes are heavy," I say. "You will sleep."

A few seconds later, the person is sleeping, but the person is also awake! The person can hear everything that I say. I give orders. The person follows my orders. Some people are easier to hypnotize than others. But I cannot hypnotize a person who does not want to be hypnotized.

A few years ago, I had an interesting idea. No one had been hypnotized just as they died. What happened to the mind and body of a person as they died? Was it possible to stop death? Soon I was able to study this idea. I had a very interesting case. Here are the facts about a special patient.

———

Mr Ernest Valdemar was a scientist, like myself. I knew him well and he liked me. Mr Valdemar was also interested in hypnotism. We talked about my idea. We talked about death and hypnotism.

Mr Valdemar was very ill. He had a disease in his lungs.

In a few months, he was going to die. He was frightened of death. His illness gave him a lot of pain. And he did not want to have a painful death. He wanted to sleep because of the pain. He wanted to be hypnotized.

"I will hypnotize you just before you die," I said.

Mr Valdemar was pleased. Then one Saturday night, he sent me a note.

Please come to my room immediately. My death is close. I cannot live another day.

I went to Mr Valdemar's room. His doctor was with him. The doctor could do nothing more for Mr Valdemar. He said goodbye to his patient and left his room. A nurse was looking after Mr Valdemar in his last hours of life.

Mr Valdemar was sitting in his bed. He was holding a pen in his hand. He was writing in a small book. His face was very pale and very, very thin. I could see the bones of his skull under his skin. And Mr Valdemar's skin was not white—it was gray.

"Hypnotize me," said the sick man. His voice was weak. "I will die before midnight. Hypnotize me now."

I moved my hands in front of Mr Valdemar's face. I had done this many times before. I did not speak. I hypnotized Mr Valdemar easily. His eyes closed immediately. Soon he was asleep.

The nurse and I laid the patient flat on the bed. Was he alive or dead? He was breathing very slowly. I held a mirror up to his lips. I saw his breath on the mirror. He was alive, but he was very weak.

"Mr Valdemar, are you asleep?" I asked.

"Yes," said the sick man. "Don't wake me. I'm dying."

After a few minutes, I asked the question again.

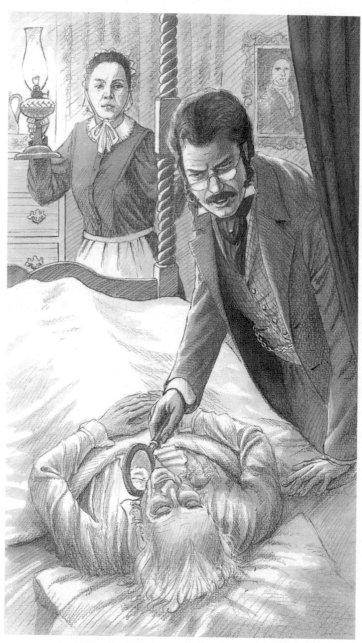

*I saw his breath on the mirror. He was alive,
but he was very weak.*

"Mr Valdemar, are you asleep?"

Mr Valdemar gave the same answer. "Yes," he replied. "Don't wake me. I'm dying."

Then his eyes opened a little. I saw only the white part of his eyes. His lips moved and I saw his teeth. Then his mouth opened and I saw his tongue. It was black. Suddenly all the breath came out of Mr Valdemar's body and he was quiet.

Mr Valdemar was dead. I was sure of this. His arms and legs were cold. He was not breathing and his heart was not beating. So I was very surprised when he spoke to me. But his voice did not come from his mouth. It came from somewhere deep in his body.

"I've been sleeping, but now I'm dead," said Mr Valdemar.

After this, Mr Valdemar did not change. He was dead, but he was not dead. The nurse closed Mr Valdemar's mouth.

Maybe he was not dead! I spoke to him again. Maybe he tried to reply, but he could not.

The next morning Mr Valdemar's doctor returned. The doctor looked at Mr Valdemar but he did not sign a death certificate.

"I can't sign the official document," he said. "I don't think that the patient is dead. You mustn't put him in a coffin. You mustn't bury him in a tomb. Wait another day."

The doctor came back the next day, and the day after that. Mr Valdemar lay on the bed. His body did not move. He did not breathe. He did not speak. He lay like a dead man. It was the sleep of death. But his body did not change. Mr Valdemar was *not* dead.

"Tell me when his body changes," said the doctor. "Soon his skin and flesh will become black and bad. Then you'll know that Mr Valdemar is dead. I will sign a death certificate when you tell me this."

How long did we wait by Mr Valdemar's body? You will not believe me! Mr Valdemar lay on the bed for seven months! His body never became black and bad. It never changed.

At the end of seven months, I made a decision. I was going to end the hypnotism. I was going to wake Mr Valdemar. This sleep of death was wrong.

I moved my hands in front of Mr Valdemar's face. I spoke in a loud and clear voice.

"You will wake up," I said.

Did Mr Valdemar's eyes move? Was he trying to open his eyes? A yellow liquid came out of his ears.

"Mr Valdemar," I said. "How do you feel? Can you speak?"

Did the patient move? Did he move his hands? I was not sure. But I *was* sure about his voice. I heard a voice that came from deep inside his body.

"Quickly! Make me sleep, or wake me up! Quickly! I tell you that I am dead."

More yellow liquid came from Mr Valdemar's body. Then there was a terrible smell. I stepped back from the bed. Then Mr Valdemar's body started to disappear. It was like black ice in hot sunlight. His body became liquid— yellow liquid that smelt terrible. Soon there was nothing left of Mr Valdemar's skin or body. There was only a pool of yellow liquid and some bones.

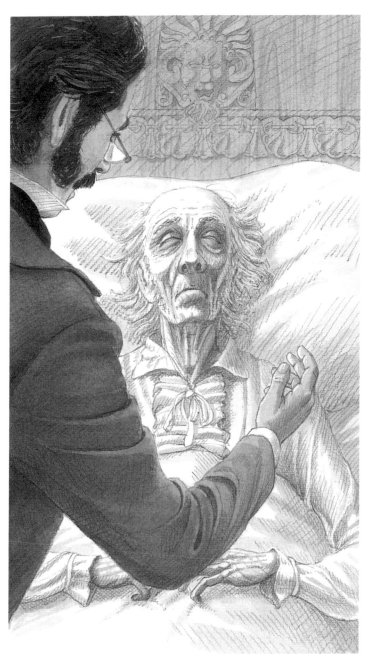

"You will wake up," I said.

THE FALL OF THE HOUSE OF USHER

It was late autumn. The weather was wet and the wind had blown all the leaves from the trees. I was riding my horse across the wet, empty land. I was traveling alone. I was going toward a dark and strange house—the House of Usher.

Why had I come to this lonely place? I knew Roderick Usher—the owner of the house. We were old friends, but we had not met for many years. A few weeks ago, I had received a letter from Roderick.

> I am ill—very ill. Please come and visit me. I am going mad! I want your help. We have been friends since we were boys. Please come!
> Roderick Usher

I had been riding all day and it was now late. The pale sun was low in the sky when I arrived at the House of Usher.

A large lake of black water surrounded the house. I stopped by the lake and looked at the house. Roderick Usher's house was a large black building. Its many windows were like empty eyes. Suddenly, I felt cold...and a little afraid.

In front of me, a narrow road went across a bridge toward the house. I walked my horse along the narrow road until I reached the walls of the house.

I knocked on the front door and a servant opened it. He took my horse to a stable. Then he led me inside the house.

Suddenly, I felt cold…and a little afraid.

We climbed many stairs to his master's room. Lamps burned along the walls, but they gave little light. The long corridors and stairways were full of dark shadows.

The servant opened a big, wooden door and I looked inside a large room.

At first, I did not recognise the man who was lying on a sofa. Then I saw that it was Roderick Usher. My friend had changed! He looked pale and ill. We were the same age, but he looked much older than me. His hair was silver-gray, and as soft as the web of a spider. I thought that Roderick was asleep because his eyes were closed. But as I entered the room, he sat up. Then he opened his eyes. They shone strangely in the weak light from the lamps.

I walked toward him.

"Welcome, my oldest and dearest friend!" he said.

But he did not shake my hand or come near me.

"Please excuse me," he said. "I don't wish to be rude. But I'm ill. I can't touch another man's hand. Please sit down. Rest a moment. A servant will take you to your room very soon. Then we shall have dinner and talk."

"I'm glad that you have come," he went on. "I have no one to talk to. My sister lives with me, but she is sick."

At that moment, a woman walked into the room. She was very pale and her eyes shone strangely. She wore a black dress with a high collar. The collar covered her long neck. She did not look toward me and she did not speak.

Roderick Usher spoke to her.

"Madeline," he said. "Madeline...this is my old friend..."

Madeline did not reply. She crossed the room slowly. Then she turned and went through a doorway. Madeline left the room as silently as she had entered it.

Roderick Usher put his hands over his face.

"My sister has a strange illness. She is neither awake nor asleep. I fear that she'll not live long."

He rang a bell and a servant took me to my room. I lay on the bed and rested for an hour before dinner. I thought about Roderick and his sister. They were both behaving strangely. I did not feel comfortable in the house. But I could not leave immediately.

I felt more comfortable at dinner. Roderick asked me about my life. He looked happier. I forgot about his sister and the strange old house.

———

Roderick Usher looked after me well for several days. We ate and drank and talked. We read books in the library. I painted pictures. Roderick played the guitar.

I did not see Madeline again. And I did not ask about her. Roderick had been alone for too long. He talked about happier days. We talked about the time when we were boys. But sometimes Roderick suddenly stopped talking. He stared in front of him. Then he turned his head to the left, then to the right. Was he listening to something? There was a look of sadness and fear on his face. I, too, felt afraid at these times.

I did not like this House of Usher. But I had come a long way to visit Roderick. I could not leave my friend. He wanted me to stay with him.

As the days passed, Roderick became more quiet and sad. One evening, he suddenly came into my room.

"Madeline is dead," he said.

I was shocked. I did not know what to say. I did not know what to do.

"I need your help," said Roderick Usher. "Madeline had been very ill. She was going to die. I knew this. But she mustn't be buried near a church. She'll lie in this house.

I'll keep her body in a room under the house. Will you help me?"

My friend's words frightened me. But I did not ask any questions. I do not know why.

We carried Madeline's body down many steps to a room under the house. No one had been in the room for many years. There were soft, gray spiders' webs hanging from the ceiling. The air was cold and damp. There were several lamps burning on the walls. But they gave little light.

A wooden coffin was in the center of the room. I helped Roderick to put his sister's body in the coffin. She wore a white dress. Her face was as white as her dress.

Roderick looked at his sister for a long time. "Madeline will rest here," he said sadly.

His face was pale and I saw the bones of his skull beneath the skin. He had not eaten for several days. Madeline was not breathing and her heart was not beating. But Madeline's body was not cold. Then I knew, and I was afraid! She was dead, but she was not dead!

Roderick fastened the lid on the coffin. Then he led me out of the room.

"No one will ever come here again," he said. "Madeline is resting now. No one will wake her."

But, from that moment, Roderick Usher never rested. He did not sleep. How long can a man live without sleep? He walked from room to room. He stared in front of him. He turned his head to the left, then to the right. Was he listening to something? Was Roderick Usher mad?

I, too, could not sleep. I lay on my bed and thought about the strange House of Usher. Suddenly, my bedroom door opened and Roderick came into the room. He was holding a lamp. His eyes were bright and wild.

"Did you hear it?" he said. "Did you see it?"

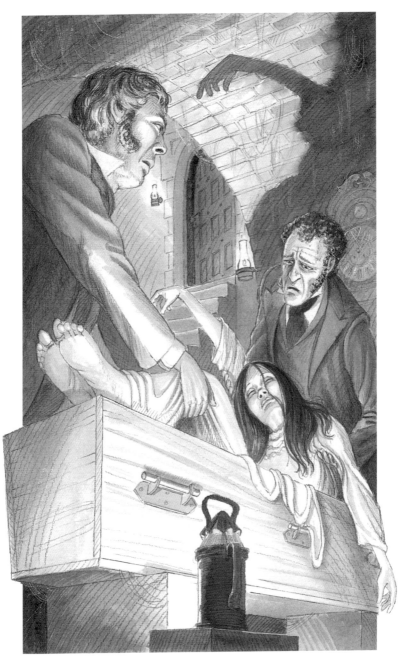

I helped Roderick to put his sister's body in the coffin.

"Hear what?" I asked. "See what?"

"You will understand soon," he said.

He pulled back the curtains and opened the window. It was dark outside and there was a storm. The wind was blowing and rain was falling. Then a flash of lightning lit the sky.

A few seconds later, there was a crash of thunder. The wind blew into the room. It screamed as it blew around the room. The door crashed shut and the flame in the lamp went out. Suddenly there was a loud noise and the floor of the room moved.

"I can hear the softest sounds," Roderick said. "I can hear everything. I can hear *her*!"

"Who can you hear?" I asked loudly. I covered my face because the wind was blowing into my eyes.

"Madeline!" Roderick replied. "I can hear her! She's coming here! She has opened her coffin. She's coming up the stairs. She's coming for *me*!"

The strong wind blew around the room again. It blew the door of the room open. Outside, lightning flashed again and again.

Suddenly I saw Madeline Usher. She was standing in the doorway. She was wearing the white dress. But it was no longer white. Her dress was covered in blood.

Madeline had broken out of her coffin! She had torn her hands and her face. There was blood on her fingers, her face and her dress.

Madeline's eyes were open but she saw nothing. She stared in front of her. She held her hands out toward her brother.

Slowly, Roderick went toward her. And she closed her blood-red arms around his body. Roderick gave a terrible scream and fell to the floor. Madeline fell with him. Their bodies lay on the floor and they did not move. They were both dead.

I ran from the terrible House of Usher. I ran across the narrow bridge. When I reached the other side of the lake, I turned around.

I looked back at the house. The wind was still blowing around the house. It made the sound of a wild animal. And I could *see* the wind! It was black and terrible! Lightning flashed in the sky and thunder crashed.

Then a bright flash of lightning hit the house and the walls broke. Slowly, the house started to fall. With a great roar, the house fell into the lake. Then the water of the lake covered the House of Usher, and there was silence.

DOWN INTO THE MAELSTRÖM

I read about the Maelström in a book and I always wanted to see it. The Maelström appears in the sea near the coast of Norway.

In the northwest of that country there is a region called Nordland. And near the coast of Nordland, there is a group of islands called Lofoten. Two of the Lofoten Islands are called Moskoe and Vurrgh. Between Moskoe and Vurrgh, there is a narrow place where the sea turns and races in a great circle. This is the Maelström—a whirlpool.

In the Maelström, the sea rises up and then falls. As the sea falls, it turns in a circle. It turns faster and faster. It is the same as water going down into a huge pipe. The Maelström is very dangerous for boats and ships. It pulls them down into the sea. Many ships have sunk and many men have died in the dangerous water.

I wanted to see the great whirlpool, so I went to Norway. When I got to Nordland, I found a guide. I paid this man to show me the Maelström. He took me to the top of a cliff early one morning.

"This is the best time to see the whirlpool," he said.

We came to the edge of the cliff and looked down. The sea was more than a thousand feet below us.

I stepped back from the edge quickly. I felt ill and afraid. I wanted to sit down. The wind was blowing very strongly and the waves of the sea crashed against the rocks below us. I thought that I was going to fall over the edge of the cliff.

"We are on the side of a mountain called Helseggen the Cloudy," said my guide. He reached out his hand and pointed across the sea toward a group of islands. "Look, those are the Lofoten. Can you see the two smallest islands? They are Moskoe and Vurrgh. No one lives there. Now listen and look at the sea between the islands."

I looked at the two smallest islands. They were black rocks. No one could live on them. I listened and heard the sound of the wind. But then I heard another sound. It was a low sound. It sounded like hundreds of huge animals were calling and running together. I could hear the sound and I could feel the sound. I could feel the low sound in my body.

"The tide is turning," said my guide. He pointed down to the sea below us. "The tide turns twice each day. Look at the sea! It is turning and moving in another direction!"

I looked to where the man was pointing. The dark water far below us was as black as oil. I watched it moving slowly. It started to rise and turn, as if it were a pot of hot water on a fire. But the seawater was not hot; it was as cold as ice. The wind blew the tops of the waves. It made many tiny bubbles of air in the water. The tiny bubbles became white foam. Soon, more and more white foam appeared on the black sea. My guide pointed toward the islands of Moskoe and Vurrgh again.

"Watch the sea between the islands!" he shouted.

Then there was another change in the sea. The water became smoother, but it did not become calmer. The dark water started to move in a huge circle. It moved very quickly. It spun around and around. The edge of the circle was white with foam. It was amazing.

"Is—is that the great whirlpool? The Maelström?" I asked.

"Yes," said my guide, "that is the terrible Maelström.

"Yes," said my guide, *"that is the terrible Maelström."*

When fishermen sail toward this coast, they look for Moskoe. They do not come closer than a mile."

"Do fishermen sail near these islands?" I asked. I could not believe this.

"Yes, they do. I did. I was a fisherman once. There are a great many fish near Moskoe."

"But isn't it too dangerous to fish here?" I asked.

"Fishermen know when the tides rise and fall. There are two times in the day when it is safe. We go out when the sea is calm and smooth. Then we come back twelve hours later."

"And is fishing always safe at those times? Are boats and ships never lost?" I asked.

"Many boats and ships are lost in the Maelström," the man said. "Fishermen make mistakes and their boats are pulled down. Sometimes larger ships are lost in the Maelström when they come too close. The sea is calm one moment, and a storm can be blowing five minutes later."

I looked at the Maelström in amazement. I could not believe it! The whirlpool was moving faster and faster. As the whirlpool moved, the water in its center dropped down. There was now a hole, or pit, in the center of the whirlpool!

"Nothing can go into that hole and come out alive," I said. "It is a huge, round mouth in the sea. That mouth will swallow everything that comes near it. It makes me afraid."

"That is true," said my guide. "The Maelström swallows ships and whales and men. But one man went into the Maelström and came out alive."

"Surely, that is impossible!" I said.

I looked at the round, black mouth in the sea. My body shook with fear. The white foam made me think of teeth.

Terrible teeth. And the noise of the wind and water! It was the noise of a monster eating rocks.

"How old do you think that I am?" asked my guide. He shouted these words. I shook my head. It was difficult to hear his voice. The noise of the Maelström was now very loud. We moved back from the edge of the cliff. We went and sat behind some rocks.

"How old do you think that I am?" the man asked again.

I did not understand the reason for his question. His hair was white and he had many lines on his face. He moved slowly. He must be an old man.

"Are you more than sixty years old?" I asked.

"No. I am forty," said my guide. "The Maelström made me old. I'll tell you my story. It happened three years ago."

This is my guide's story. I am writing his words.

———

One day in the summer, my brothers and I went out in our fishing boat. It was seven o'clock in the morning of July 10th. The sea was calm and smooth. We sailed past Moskoe Island to look for fish.

There were many fish in the sea that day. We caught a large number of them and loaded them into our boat. We were very busy and we forgot how many hours had passed.

In summer, we have nearly twenty hours of daylight in Norway. The nights are short. There are only four hours of darkness. When I looked at my watch, I saw that it was six o'clock in the evening.

We had to pass Moskoe Island at seven o'clock. That was the time when the tide turned. It was safe at seven o'clock that day. We were about an hour away from Moskoe. We started to return home immediately.

A storm came suddenly. Dark clouds covered the sky

and the wind started to blow. Our boat raced before the storm. Faster and faster, we sailed toward home and safety.

When I looked to the northeast, I saw Moskoe Island. The sea was moving very quickly, but it was almost the safe time of the day. It was almost seven o'clock. I was sure of this. I took my watch out of my pocket again and looked at it. Then I had a terrible shock. My watch still showed six o'clock. It had stopped!

My brothers were in the front of the boat. I called to them.

"The Maelström!" I shouted. "My watch was wrong! We are too late!"

It was not the safe time of day. It was the time when the great whirlpool opened like a mouth in the sea. We were going to die!

Our boat shook. It shook as if it were a dog throwing water off its body. Then the boat suddenly became still.

A few seconds later, the tide picked up our boat and started turning it. It pulled us into the circle of white water around the edge of the whirlpool.

Our boat moved slowly and steadily around the edge of the whirlpool. It circled many times. Each time that our boat circled, it moved a little closer to the great mouth in the sea. From the edge of the circle, the wall of the pit was as steep as a cliff. I had to look down at it. I could not turn my head away.

Around and around we went. My brothers held onto the mast in the center of the boat. We could not speak. The noise of the wind and water was too loud.

I could not hold onto the mast. I held onto a wooden barrel. It was our barrel of drinking water. The barrel was almost empty.

Our boat moved faster and faster. Now, the clouds had

disappeared from the sky and we saw the moon.

I thought that we had been in the whirlpool for many hours. The hours of darkness are between two and seven o'clock in the morning. Could we live a little longer? The safe time of the day was seven o'clock. Could we live for three, or maybe four hours more?

The answer was no. The moon showed us the black mouth in the sea. We were going to fall into that mouth.

But we did not fall. The boat did not fall suddenly from the wall of water. We moved down smoothly and steadily.

I had time to think about death—my death. I thought about the water going into my mouth and lungs. I was going to drown. Was the sea going to take our bodies and keep them? Or was it going to throw our bodies back onto the land?

I looked down into the black pit. Our boat was on the side of the wall of water. The wall of water was turning faster and faster. I looked straight down the pipe of water but I did not fall. We were moving so quickly in a circle, that we did not fall. I was amazed.

The air raced past me. I was on the edge of death, but I was alive. It was strange. I was excited.

But the fear of death fell on my brothers. They took a rope and tied themselves to the mast in the center of the boat. I also took a piece of rope. I tied the rope around my body and onto the barrel.

Where was the bottom of the sea? It could not be far. And I knew that there were sharp rocks at the bottom of the sea. We were going to be cut and broken on the rocks!

Our boat moved lower and lower down the black pipe. Then the boat moved to the left and the right. It shook. I was thrown into the black water of the pit. But I did not sink beneath the water because I was tied to the barrel.

I had time to think about my death. I was going to drown.

The barrel stayed on the top of the water.

I saw the boat and my brothers fall down into the pit. We were turning around in the whirlpool. Then the boat disappeared and I started to rise. The barrel moved up slowly. And it took me with it.

Then, suddenly, I was no longer in danger. One moment, I was on the wall of water. The next moment, I was on the top of flat, smooth water. The sea had changed. It was calm. The whirlpool had disappeared. I was no longer looking down. I was looking up. I was looking up at the sky.

It was dawn and the sun was shining. Sunlight shone from behind the mountain, Helseggen the Cloudy. Fishermen were sailing their boats toward me. They pulled me from the water.

No one believed my story. My brothers never returned. Our boat never returned. And my friends and family did not know me. I now looked twenty years older. My black hair had become white. Fear had made lines on my face.

THE MASQUE OF THE RED DEATH

A terrible disease came to this country. The illness was called the Red Death. No one was safe. Soon many people were sick. There was no help—no cure. The Red Death killed half of the people in this land.

Prince Prospero—the ruler of this country—wanted to escape from the terrible disease. He called all his courtiers to his castle on the top of a hill. When all of the most powerful people in the land were inside the castle, the gates and doors were closed. They were fastened and no one could get in or out.

Prince Prospero had plenty of food inside the castle. And there was plenty of wine to drink. He did not think about the rest of the people in his land. Prince Prospero told his courtiers to enjoy themselves.

"Forget about the Red Death," he said. "The disease is outside the castle walls. I don't want to think about the Red Death. I don't want to hear about the Red Death. I don't want to see the Red Death. I want everyone to be happy!"

The prince prepared a masque for his courtiers. There was going to be music for dancing. There was going to be wonderful food to eat. There was going to be good wine to drink. Dancers and singers were going to entertain the guests. Everyone was going to wear masks. Their faces were going to be hidden by the masks.

There were seven special rooms in the castle. Each room was a different color. And each room had a great window in one of its walls. The glass in each of these windows was a different color. At night, a fire burned outside each window. The light of the flames shone through the windows and the rooms were lit with colored light.

These rooms were together in a line. The prince and his courtiers went from one room to the next room. They sang and danced. They laughed. They ate and drank.

The first room was blue—the color of the sky. The chairs and the carpet were blue. The furniture was blue. The glass in the window was blue.

The second room was purple—the color of dark wine. The chairs and couches were covered with purple cloth. The window glass was purple.

The third room was green—the color of leaves. It had green glass in its window.

The fourth room was orange—the color of the sun at sunset. The fifth room was as white as snow. The sixth room was violet—the color at the edge of a rainbow.

The seventh and last room was black—as black as night. Black curtains hung on the walls. The carpets on the floor were black.

But the window in this room was red—the color of blood. The light that came through the window was the color of blood.

There was also a clock in the seventh room. It was a large old clock. Its pendulum swung backward and forward slowly. A bell in the clock rang every hour. The metal bell made a low noise. Everyone in the castle heard the bell. Every hour, they stopped and listened to the clock.

When the bell rang, the musicians stopped playing music. The dancers stopped dancing. The courtiers stopped eating and drinking. The faces of the men and women became pale. They held their hands in front of their eyes. When they heard the clock, they became

Every hour, they stopped and listened to the clock.

afraid. When the clock was silent, they took their hands from their faces and they laughed. Then the musicians started playing again. The dancers danced. Everyone ate and drank. They forgot about the clock until the next hour.

Prince Prospero was pleased. This was his finest masque. He thought of nothing but the masque. The courtiers enjoyed themselves. Their only thoughts were about the food, drink, music and dancing.

The masque had started in the afternoon. The courtiers did not worry about the clock at first. The bell rang once. It rang twice. It rang three times. The courtiers stopped for only a few moments as the bell rang. Then the masque continued.

The guests walked from room to room. When night came, fires were lit behind the great windows. Light shone through the glass. The light was the color of each of the windows—blue, purple, green, orange, white and violet.

But one room was empty. No one wanted to enter the seventh room. This room had red light coming through its window. And it had the great clock.

The bell of the clock rang ten times. Everyone stopped. Then they ate, danced and drank again. Eleven o'clock came. The courtiers stopped for a longer time. But soon they were enjoying themselves once more. Finally, the bell rang twelve times. The courtiers stopped and waited. They all listened as the bell rang twelve times. Midnight.

Suddenly they saw a stranger. No one had seen this stranger's mask before. Who was this person? No one could enter or leave the castle. How had the stranger entered?

The stranger wore a long white gown. He wore the clothes of a dead man in a tomb. His mask was terrible and frightening. He had the face of a dead man. There was blood on the mask. And there was blood on the stranger's clothes.

Prince Prospero was not pleased. He did not want to remember the Red Death. Who had come wearing a mask that reminded them of the Red Death?

"Take him!" shouted the prince. "Kill him!"

Several men moved toward the stranger. The stranger looked at the men. They stopped walking. Was there a mask on the stranger's face? Or was the sign of disease on the stranger's face? The men were afraid.

"Take him!" shouted the prince again. "Kill him!"

But no one touched the stranger. Everyone moved away from him. The prince was angry.

The stranger walked from the blue room into the purple room. Everyone moved away from the stranger with the mask of the Red Death. Everyone was afraid.

Prince Prospero followed the stranger from the blue room to the purple room. He followed him from the green room to the orange room. He followed the stranger from the white room to the violet room.

There was only one more room. The stranger stood in the black room. He stood in front of the great clock. The hands of the clock had stopped at midnight. The bell was never going to ring again. The red light from the window fell on the stranger and the clock. The red light was the color of blood.

Prince Prospero pulled a knife from his belt. He went into the black room. He was going to kill the stranger.

The red light fell on the stranger, and he turned toward Prince Prospero. The stranger was not wearing a mask!

Prince Prospero cried out in pain. The knife fell from his hand. The prince fell onto the ground in front of the clock. He was dead.

Then every one of the courtiers fell onto the floor. Their bodies shook. Blood came from their ears, their eyes and their noses. The floor became red with blood. They cried in fear as they died.

Prince Prospero no longer ruled in the castle. The castle had a new master. Red Death was the ruler now.

THE OBLONG BOX

My home is in New York. But several years ago, I stayed in Charleston, South Carolina, for a few months. At the end of my visit, I returned to New York by ship.

In those days, we traveled by sailing ships. Sailing ships took about a week to sail from Charleston to New York. When the winds and the tides were good, the journey took six days. If there was little wind and we had to wait for a good tide, the journey took eight days.

There were no regular days and times for ships to sail. Passengers went to a shipping office. They asked a clerk where ships were going. The clerk told the passengers the names of the ships and their destinations. Then he wrote the passengers' names beside the names of the ships. The captains of the ships looked at this list. Then they sent messages to the passengers when their ships were ready.

A ship was going to sail from Charleston in the middle of June. Its destination was going to be New York. I booked a cabin on the ship. Then I waited in a hotel.

I wanted to find out the names of the other travelers. The list of the passengers' names was kept in the shipping office. So I went to the shipping office and I looked at the list. There was one name on the list that I knew— Cornelius Wyatt. Cornelius and I were students together at university.

A few months earlier, I had heard news about Cornelius Wyatt. A friend in New York wrote me a letter. Cornelius had married a beautiful and charming young woman. I wanted to meet Mrs Wyatt. I had never seen her.

Why were Cornelius and his wife in Charleston?

Cornelius was an artist. He painted pictures. He also bought and sold paintings. Old paintings were worth a lot of money in New York. Was that the answer to my question?

Maybe Cornelius had found a valuable painting in Charleston. There were many old families in South Carolina. The families had brought many paintings from Europe. Was Cornelius taking an old painting to New York?

I was going to find the answer to both these questions soon. We were traveling together on the same ship.

A captain sent a message. His ship was going to sail to New York the next day—June 15th. I went to the harbor and boarded his ship. I looked at the list of passengers and their cabins.

Cornelius Wyatt had booked three cabins. He had the two cabins opposite mine and the cabin beside mine. He was not traveling alone. He had three ladies with him— his wife and his two sisters. The two sisters were in a cabin opposite my own cabin. I expected Cornelius and his wife to take the second cabin opposite mine. But who was going to be in the third cabin?

I was surprised when I met Mr and Mrs Wyatt at last. Cornelius looked ill and he was not pleased to see me.

"My friend, we have much to talk about," I said. "And is this your charming and beautiful wife?"

The lady with Cornelius was wearing a veil. The thin material covered her face and I could not see her clearly. But she said "Good morning" to me politely. She spoke slowly—she had the accent of South Carolina. She did not speak with a New York accent.

Cornelius did not speak to me. He took his wife into the cabin opposite mine and shut the door.

"Cornelius was very rude," I thought. "But he is an artist. Artists can be very selfish. We will talk later. But who is staying in the third cabin? Maybe a servant will be in the cabin beside me."

Two men brought a box onto the ship. It was an oblong box, about six feet long.

The men took the box to Cornelius Wyatt's third cabin—the cabin beside mine. They put the box down on the floor while they opened the door. The words WYATT and NEW YORK were written on the top of the box.

I watched the two men carry the oblong box into the cabin. Then I heard the men talking. The walls of the cabin were thin and I could hear their conversation.

"It smells bad, doesn't it?" said one man.

"Yes," said the other man. "What's in it, do you think?"

The two men left the cabin and closed the door.

I wanted to look at the strange box more carefully. But I could not do that. First, I must speak to Cornelius.

There were paintings in the box. That is what I believed. But I wanted to see them. What had Cornelius found in Charleston? Maybe the paintings were secret and valuable.

I saw Cornelius later in the evening. All the passengers were in the dining-room eating dinner. I tried to speak to Cornelius. But he did not want to talk. He was rude to me. Also he was not hungry. He ate nothing. Was he ill?

"Well," I said. "We're old friends, but you're behaving badly."

Cornelius said nothing. I was angry with him now. I wanted to be rude too.

"Are you worried about the things in your box?" I asked. "I have guessed what is inside it. But I won't tell anyone."

The words WYATT and NEW YORK were
written on the top of the box.

I said the words. Then I wished that I had not said them. Suddenly, Cornelius Wyatt's face became very pale. His eyes were large and bright. Was he ill? Or was he mad? Cornelius Wyatt suddenly fell to the floor and was still. He had fainted.

The captain and two sailors helped Cornelius to his cabin. I went to my own cabin and tried to sleep. But I could not rest.

I heard someone open the door of the cabin beside me. Had Cornelius gone into the cabin? Had he gone to look at his pictures? I heard the sound of metal on wood. Was Cornelius opening the box?

Maybe I slept a little then. Maybe I dreamt. I thought that I heard the sound of someone crying.

Cornelius stayed in that cabin. He did not want to come out. Food was taken to him. He did not eat it.

"Those paintings must be extremely valuable," I said to myself. "Cornelius cannot leave them for a minute."

Then I thought of another reason for my old friend's strange behavior. Mrs Wyatt did not stay in her cabin. She came out and talked to the other passengers. I saw her in the dining room.

I was very surprised. I had been told that Mrs Wyatt was beautiful and charming. But she was neither beautiful nor charming. And she was not young. My friend had said that Mrs Wyatt was from New York. But she spoke with a South Carolina accent.

Was this the reason for my friend's strange behavior? Had Cornelius made a mistake? Had he married the wrong woman? Was he sad and upset about this?

The door of the cabin was locked and Cornelius did not come out. What was he going to do when we reached New York?

Then something happened and I forgot Cornelius Wyatt's secrets. A few days after we left Charleston, there was a storm. The wind blew and the sea became rough. The waves grew taller and taller. It was a very bad storm. It blew the ship south—back toward Charleston.

The wind was very strong. It blew all night. The ship moved from side to side. It almost turned over. The mast broke. The captain could not steer the ship and it went toward the shore. The ship hit some of the sharp black rocks on the coastline and it started to sink. Soon seawater came along the corridors and into the cabins.

"Leave the ship!" the captain shouted to everyone. "Quickly! Go to the small boats! Do not stop to take anything with you!"

I ran out of my cabin and I saw Mrs Wyatt. I saw Cornelius Wyatt's two sisters. The sailors helped us to get into a rowboat. There were fifteen of us in the boat. The captain was with us.

It was daylight, but black clouds were in the sky. We could see land two miles away. The wind was blowing toward the land.

We looked up at the ship. It was now low in the water. The ship was sinking. Soon it was going to be under the sea.

Suddenly we saw Cornelius Wyatt. We had forgotten him. Cornelius was pulling the oblong box toward the side of the ship. He was pulling the box toward our rowboat. His eyes were wild. He was terribly frightened.

"Mr Wyatt!" shouted the captain. "Get into this boat now! The ship is sinking!"

"I cannot leave my box," Cornelius replied. "I must get into the boat with my box."

"No!" shouted the captain. "We can only take you. You

cannot bring your box. Quick! Get into the boat! The ship is sinking!"

"I cannot leave my box!" Cornelius shouted again.

"Is your box more important than your life?" I shouted.

Cornelius looked at me. I saw madness in his eyes. He hated me. He hated my question.

"Yes! Yes! Yes!" Cornelius shouted.

He lifted the box onto the side of the ship. As he pushed it over the side, he held onto it. The box and Cornelius fell into the sea. Both the man and the box went straight down into the water. Cornelius and the oblong box did not come up again.

"Get the boat away from the side of the ship!" shouted the captain. We pulled on the oars and the rowboat moved away from the sinking ship. In a few minutes, the ship had sunk beneath the sea.

The wind blew our rowboat to the shore. At last, we were safe.

———

A month later, I met the captain again. We talked about the storm and our escape from the sinking ship. We talked about Cornelius and the oblong box.

"It was a mistake to bring that box onto the ship," the captain said. "The box brought bad luck to the ship. I did not want to take the box."

"What was in the box?" I asked.

"The body of Mr Wyatt's dead wife," the captain replied. "Mr Wyatt's wife died suddenly on June 14th. She died in Charleston, on the day before we sailed. Mr Wyatt had to return to New York. And he wanted to take his dead wife's body with him. None of the other captains wanted to carry a dead body in their ships. Some people believe that it is bad luck to keep a dead person on a ship.

"Is your box more important than your life?" I shouted.

But Mr Wyatt asked me again and again. He became very upset. At last I agreed. He lied to the shipping clerk and the other passengers. He said that there were valuable paintings in the box."

"So who was the Mrs Wyatt that I met?" I asked him.

"She was his servant," said the captain. "Wyatt loved his beautiful wife very much. Only I knew the truth."

POINTS FOR UNDERSTANDING

Points for Understanding

THE PIT AND THE PENDULUM

1 How does the storyteller first find out about the pit?
2 How is Time going to kill the storyteller?
3 How many seconds pass between each swing of the pendulum
  at the end of the torture?
4 How do the rats help the storyteller?

THE GOLD BUG

1 Describe William Legrand.
2 How is fire important in this story?
3 What are the two meanings for "a glass"?
4 What are: (a) the death's head (b) the devil's seat (c) a pickax
  (d) a tape measure?
5 Why does Legrand think that the number 8 is E?
6 Look again at the code. What does this message mean?
  °6(5;8) 3‡0†8* ;(85)?(8

THE FACTS IN THE CASE OF MR VALDEMAR

1 Mr Valdemar wants to be hypnotized. Why?
2 Why does the storyteller hold a mirror to Mr Valdemar's lips?
3 Why will the doctor not sign the death certificate?
4 When does the storyteller end the hypnotism? Why?
5 What happens next?

THE FALL OF THE HOUSE OF USHER

1 The storyteller says: "At first, I did not recognise the man who was lying on a sofa." How has the storyteller's friend changed?
2 Describe Madeline Usher.
3 What do Roderick and the storyteller do after Madeline's death?
4 What happens to: (a) Madeline (b) Roderick (c) the House of Usher?
5 Give your reasons for the behavior of the Ushers.

DOWN INTO THE MAELSTRÖM

1 The guide points down to the sea below them.
   What is happening?
2 What is foam?
3 Where does the whirlpool appear?
4 When do the fisherman and his brothers know that they are all in terrible danger?
5 Why do you think that the fisherman does not die in the Maelström?
6 Write four sentences about the sea. In two sentences, the sea is dangerous. In the other sentences, there is no danger. Use these words: *wind calm strongly smooth still slowly waves steadily rough.*

THE MASQUE OF THE RED DEATH

1 What is the difference between a masque and a mask?
2 What happens at midnight?
3 There are several things that are colored red in this story.
   Name four of them.
4 Why has the stranger come to the castle? Give your reasons.

THE OBLONG BOX

1 What is the destination of the ship that is sailing from
  Charleston on June 15th?
2 Why is the storyteller surprised when he meets Cornelius
  Wyatt's wife?
3 The storyteller talks to Cornelius about the strange box.
  He says: "I can guess what is inside it." What happens next?
4 What does the storyteller believe is in the box?
5 "Is your box more important than your life?"
  How does Cornelius behave when he hears this question?
  What happens next?

Exercises

Words From The Story

Put each word in the box next to the correct meaning.

> ~~mast~~ guitar compass skull telescope web beetle pirate
> treasure branch shovel lantern mask scythe whale
> spider bridge rainbow oar lamp creek coffin
> hourglass pendulum

1	A tall piece of wood or metal that holds the sails of a ship.	*mast*
2	A sharp tool for cutting grass or corn.	
3	A small inlet on the coast where the sea comes in.	
4	A long, round instrument with special glass inside. You use it to look at things which are a long way away.	
5	A person who robs ships.	
6	A light that you can carry at night. A candle burns inside it.	
7	The arm of a tree.	
8	A half circle of seven colours that you sometimes see in the sky after rain.	
9	A tool which is like a spade. You use it to dig earth.	
10	A very big animal that lives in the sea.	
11	An old instrument that uses sand to show the time.	

12 A thin net.

13 Gold, silver, jewels or other things that are worth a lot of money. In stories, it is often stolen or buried.

14 A thing that is built across a road or river. It helps you get across.

15 A musical instrument with strings. You play it with your hands.

16 An instrument with a needle that always points north.

17 A box that holds a dead body.

18 A thing which you wear over your face to hide or protect it.

19 An insect with hard wings and a shiny body.

20 A long piece of wood with a flat end. You use it to move a boat.

21 A small animal with eight legs.

22 The bones of the head – of a person or animal.

23 A light you use at night. It burns oil.

24 A heavy weight at the end of a chain which moves backwards and forwards.

Word Focus 1

The *-bow* in rainbow has the same sound as *go* and *so* – not the sound of *how* and *now*. Put the words in the box into the correct column.

pound   low   down   brown   no   ground   toe   cow   town   throw

Group 1	Group 2
go / so	*how / now*

Word Focus 2

The words *sow, bow* and *row* give problems in English. They can have the Group 1 or the Group 2 sound (see page 79). Their meaning is different. For the sentences below, write whether the word has the Group 1 sound or the Group 2 sound.

Sentence	Group
1 Farmers *sow* seeds in the fields.	*1*
2 A big noise is called a *row*.	
3 Legrand told Jupiter to *row* the boat.	
4 Robin Hood had a *bow* and arrows.	
5 People *bow* their heads when they pray.	
6 A female pig is called a *sow*.	

Grammar Focus 1: (*stop doing something / stop to do something*)

Make sentences with *stopped* and the correct form of the verb shown.

Example 1	We were driving. Our car needed gas. We stopped at a gas station.
get gas	*We stopped to get some gas.*
Example 2	I was running. I was tired. I didn't run any more.
run	*I stopped running.*

1	I was riding. I saw a great house. I stopped my horse. I looked.
look at house	
2	Roderick Usher talked and talked for hours. He never stopped.
talk	
3	The doctor stopped at Mr Valdemar's room. He came to examine the patient.
examine patient	
4	I lay on the floor. I did not breathe. The pendulum no longer moved.
pendulum move	
5	Prince Prospero's guests heard the clock strike. They did not dance.
dance	
6	I looked at my watch. The time was 6 o'clock. About an hour later I looked again. The time was still 6 o'clock.
work	

7	Wyatt stopped by his cabin door. He took the oblong box.
take box	
8	Mr Valdemar was dead. He no longer breathed.
breathe	

Grammar Focus 2: (*a* and *the*)

Complete the gaps with *a* or *the*.

[1]"....*The*.... Maelström!" I shouted. "My watch was wrong! We are too late!"

It was not [2]............... safe time of day. It was [3]............... time when [4]............... great whirlpool opened like [5]............... mouth in [6]............... sea. We were going to die!

Our boat shook. It shook like [7]............... dog drying itself. Then [8]............... boat became still.

A few seconds later, [9]............... tide picked up our boat and started turning it. It pulled us into [10]............... circle of white water around [11]............... edge of [12]............... whirlpool.

Our boat moved slowly and steadily around [13]............... edge of [14]............... whirlpool. It circled many times. Each time that our boat circled, it moved [15]............... little closer to [16]............... great mouth in [17]............... sea. From [18]............... edge of [19]............... circle, [20]............... wall of [21]............... pit was as steep as [22]............... cliff. I had to look down at it. I could not turn my head away.

Around and around we went. My brothers held onto [23]............... mast in [24]............... center of [25]............... boat. We could not speak. [26]............... noise of [27]............... wind and water was too loud.

I could not hold onto [28]............... mast. I held onto [29]............... wooden barrel. It was our barrel of drinking water. [30]............... barrel was almost empty. I tied myself to [31]............... barrel with [32]............... piece of rope.

83

Word Focus 3: (shapes)

Write the shape names.

| rectangle | circle | triangle | square |

1	2	3	4

The word *oblong* is old-fashioned. What shape is an oblong?

Grammar Focus 3: (nouns and adjectives)

Write sentences using the correct adjective.

Example	noun	The shape of the room was a circle.
	adjective	*The room was circular.*

1	noun	The shape of the box was a rectangle.
	adjective	
2	noun	The shape of the blade was a curve.
	adjective	
3	noun	The shape of the room was a square.
	adjective	
4	noun	The shape of the pit was a circle.
	adjective	
5	noun	The shape of the window was a triangle.
	adjective	
6	noun	The measurement was in a straight line.
	adjective	

7	noun	The side of the whirlpool was a slope.
	adjective	
8	noun	The land around the lake was a marsh.
	adjective	

Making Sentences 1

Write sentences using *looked like* and *sounded like*.

Example 1	The windows of the House of Usher were empty eyes.
You write	*The windows looked like empty eyes.*
Example 2	The Maelström made the noise of thunder.
You write	*The Maelström sounded like thunder.*

1 The cell was a tomb.

2 The animals made the noise of rats.

3 The picture made me think of Time.

4 The blade resembled the pendulum of an old clock.

5 I thought I heard the noise of guns.

6 The voice seemed to be the voice of Mr Valdemar.

7 Madeline Usher was a walking corpse.

8   The walls of The Maelström were glass.

_____

_____

Making Sentences 2

Write sentences using *took*.

| **Example** | The ship left Charleston on Saturday and arrived in New York the next Friday. |
| You write | *The journey took six days. / It took the ship six days to reach New York.* |

1   We left the island at 4 pm and reached the hill at 6 pm.

_____

2   The trial began on 1 March and ended on 5 March.

_____

3   It seemed a long trip. We spent two hours going to the hill and two hours coming back again.

_____

4   The fishing trip will last for half a day.

_____

_____

5   The ship sank in a few minutes.

_____

6   The passengers reached the shore in an hour.

_____

The Gold Bug Cipher

Edgar Allan Poe used these marks in his secret message from Captain Kidd.

A	B	C	D	E	F	G	H	I	J	K	L	M	N	O	P	Q	R	S	T	U	V	W	X	Y	Z
5	2	-	†	8	1	3	4	6			0	9	*	‡	.			(	)	;	?	¶	]		:

We do not know the letters J, K, Q, X or Z because they do not appear in the message.

English uses the letter E most often. After that, the sequence is:

T A O N I R S H D L C U P F M W Y G B V K X Q J Z

E, T, A and O are the most frequent letters in British English. X, Q, J and Z are the least frequent.

Can you work out this message? It is written in the Gold Bug Cipher.

8†35(5005* .‡8 ?*‡8();‡‡† 5 0‡; 52‡?;)8-(8;
](6;6*3 2?; 48 –‡?0† *‡; †8)-(628 46) 98;4‡†)

_____

_____

_____

_____

Published by Macmillan Heinemann ELT
Between Towns Road, Oxford OX4 3PP
Macmillan Heinemann ELT is an imprint of
Macmillan Publishers Limited
Companies and representatives throughout the world
Heinemann is a registered trademark of Harcourt Education, used under licence

ISBN 1–4050–7533–3
EAN 978–1–4050–7535–0

This retold version of the stories: *The Pit and the Pendulum*, *The Gold Bug*,
The Facts in the Case of M. *Valdemar*, *The Fall of the House of Usher*,
Descent into the Maelström, *The Masque of the Red Death* and *The Oblong
Box* by Edgar Allan Poe was retold by Stephen Colbourn for Macmillan
Readers
First published 2005
Text © Stephen Colbourn 2005
Design and illustration © Macmillan Publishers Limited 2005
This version first published 2005

All rights reserved; no part of this publication may be
reproduced, stored in a retrieval system, transmitted in any
form, or by any means, electronic, mechanical, photocopying,
recording, or otherwise, without the prior written permission of
the publishers.

Illustrated by John Dillow and Martin Sanders
Cover by Corbis/Jean-Pierre Lescourret

Printed in Spain by Edelvives

2009 2008 2007 2006 2005
10 9 8 7 6 5 4 3 2 1